Stop!

Look up the road.

Look down the road.

2

Stop!

Here comes a car.

Look up the road.

Look down the road.

Stop!

Here comes a bus.

Look up the road.

Look down the road.

Stop!

Here comes a truck.

Look up the road.

Look down the road.

Stop!

Here comes a van.

Look up the road.

Look down the road.

Stop!

Here comes a bike.

Look up the road.

Look down the road.

Stop!

Here comes a motor-bike.

13

Look up the road.

Look down the road.

We can cross now.